W9-BOA-699

A GARDENER'S JOURNAL

GA

A
RDENER'S
JOURNAL

With Text by Elvin McDonald

MUSEUM OF FINE ARTS, BOSTON

First published in 1992 by
The Museum of Fine Arts, Boston
Department of Retail Publications
295 Huntington Avenue
Boston, Massachusetts 02115

ISBN 0-87846-349-6

Production coordinator: Lori Stein, Layla Productions
Cover design by Christopher Frame

Research for quotations by Ruth Birnkrant and Sandra Still
Quotation on page 59 from *Collected Poems 1900-1935*,
by T.S. Eliot, copyright 1936 by Harcourt Brace & World, Inc.

PRINTED AND BOUND IN HONG KONG

CONTENTS

HOW TO USE THIS BOOK

GARDENING IS NOT JUST a summer activity. It's a process that is pondered upon and thought about throughout the fading months of fall, the cold winter months, and the excitement of the coming thaw. A gardener needs more than just a diary to record day-to-day activities. A gardener needs a planning *guide;* something to refer to throughout the year for advice, reminders, and resources.

We've arranged this guide in five distinct sections, each to help you plan your gardening year. And because gardening *is* a yearly activity, we've presented the information in a month-to-month format.

FIRST SECTION: GARDEN NOTES

At the beginning of each month, gardening expert Elvin McDonald provides you with gardening notes for the month. He includes a listing of what's in bloom, and advice on what to prune, plant, mulch or compost. Of special interest are his time saving tips: for example, the more time you spend in April and May planning to sow thinly, the less time you will have to spend in the summer months thinning overcrowded vegetables. And his advice is focused to all garden types, whether yours is a vegetable garden, an annual or perennial flower garden, a landscaped shrubbery garden, or the city-dweller's houseplant garden.

SECOND SECTION: PLANNING YOUR GARDEN

The second section of each month is devoted to planning your garden. Here is room to list your new purchases for that month, or what you plan to purchase, what you've planted or plan to plant, and space to keep track of what's new that's in bloom.

SECTION THREE: A DAY-BY-DAY RECORD

The bulk of each month is devoted to space to record your daily garden activities, your successes and failures. We've included space for you to record the weather conditions, noting the high and low temperatures, and precipitation, if any, on that day. This is a journal that can be used for more than one year. We expect that most gardeners will go back to these notes to improve next year's garden, or to remember lost details of the previous garden year.

SECTION FOUR: RESOURCES

At the back of the journal, we've provided you with a blank directory so you can keep track of your purchases, whether from a catalog, wholesale supply house, or gardening shop.

SECTION FIVE: GARDEN GRID

Also at the back of the book is a grid so you can plan your garden layout. We suggest you make several photocopies of this spread. The gardeners we know are forever changing their minds, and making new layouts!

We hope you enjoy *A Gardener's Journal.* Throughout we've provided beautiful artwork from many eras and many different climes. Perhaps Monet's garden will inspire yours, or Stella's cactus will encourage you to take a stab at South Western–style cactus gardening!

INTRODUCTION

EVERY GARDENER NEEDS a diary, if for no other reason than to make diagrams or sketches indicating what is planted where. This responds to the reality that labels in the garden almost always perish before the information on them is needed; that eventually you will forget the names and where the plants originated, at precisely the moment when this information is desperately needed; and besides, plantings with name sticks and small placards set about have a tendency to look more like scientific studies or graveyards than gardens.

Dedicated Northerners say that they garden in the North partly to experience the four seasons as distinct and refreshingly different from each other. This view implies that tropical gardens have no such seasonality, which is not true, for gardens and plants in all climates warm and cold, outdoors and in, are inextricably tied to day length. Plants expand, grow actively, in response to days that are increasingly long and hence remind them of Spring. They flower and bear fruit according to their individual relationship to the beginning of Summer. With the arrival of the longest day, they sense that their days of more light are over; less and less becomes the rule. By the time of Autumn, outdoor plants are hardening, toughening up for winter, the coming season of semidormancy, "rest" in human terms, hibernation for bears.

There are always factors other than light that determine how and when a plant grows, but everywhere the gardener has a need to respond daily and within the framework of the current season. Thus broken down, the myriad activities that result in a cultivated garden of beauty and fruitfulness can be grasped, giving a sense of order in chaos, a driving force for gardeners in general.

Or is it? To be a gardener is almost inevitably to be a self-styled philosopher, which explains another primitive need for *A Gardener's Diary*. The gardener is accustomed to putting down and letting go, how else to explain the hopeful burial of seeds and bulbs, the microsensitive response to the preciousness of roots? Folklore and sayings thrust through the gardener's consciousness as surely as seedlings poke through the earth's crust. Here in these pages such thoughts may be set out and let go as well.

At the practical bottom line, every gardener needs to be reminded of what to do and when, and for each month of *A Gardener's Diary* there is a checklist of timely activities, followed by a list of principal plants in bloom. This is needed in part because a gardener's tasks at any given moment may not be done again for a year or maybe not for several seasons. If each year's entries are dated, the *Diary* will become increasingly valuable as it permits comparisons and converts to a general pattern of repeating success rather than failure.

Elvin McDonald

A GARDENER'S JOURNAL

JANUARY

GARDEN NOTES

If you take a vacation to the sun, visit the local botanic garden or arboretum. Pick up seeds of any tropical plants that appeal; they usually sprout easily and can become unusual indoor plants in the North. Cover each type of seed to the depth of its own thickness, using fresh potting mix or a commercial product labeled for seed sowing. Maintain evenly moist and constantly warm, 70-75 F. Seedlings appear in one to six weeks and will then need a sunny window or fluorescent-light garden.

Houseplants

A snow-covered landscape means more reflected light indoors, a benefit to houseplants and any seeds you may be starting (such as *Begonia semperflorens*, hybrid geraniums and the fancy frilled Grandiflora petunia). Any time the weather dictates lots of furnace heating, houseplants need more watering than usual and a boost in the humidity, from a humidifier or from simmering a big pot of water (add herbs, potpourri or essential oil to impart fragrance at the same time you are adding humidity to the air of your home); pebble humidity trays also help. Relieve cabin fever by planting some seeds; give large houseplants a lukewarm sponge bath, or a shower in the tub so they'll be rain fresh.

> *A gardener's work is never at an end.*
> *It begins with the year, and continues to the next;*
> *he prepares the ground and then he sows it; after*
> *that he plants and then he gathers the fruit.*
>
> JOHN EVELYN, "Kalendarum Hortense"

Flowers

Herbaceous crowns are often bared in a winter thaw. Take a walk and check about for any that may have heaved from the ground by the action of frost. Add soil or compost over any exposed roots.

Trees

Ideal time to assess deciduous trees, while their branches are bare and the structure is most plainly revealed. Make notes in your garden notebook of any pruning that needs doing, by you or by a professional service. In the event of a heavy, wet snow that sticks, walk about the property and knock off as much as possible from evergreens, hedges, shrubbery, younger trees; use a long-handled broom or what-have-you and remove the snow as soon as possible.

Edibles

Herbs are in renaissance, and there have hardly ever been so many different vegetables and fruits under cultivation — new hybrids, old hybrids, heirloom varieties. Bear in mind (pun not intended): grow at home the kinds of edibles that aren't suited to mass commercial production and long-distance shipping. This means you won't be competing with the professionals but rather growing flavorsome kinds they can't. Plan with the idea that vegetables, herbs and other edibles can be used as decorative, ornamental parts of the landscape and needn't be relegated to a serviceable plot at the back of the property. No piece of ground in the earth to call your own? Plan to grow vegetables in containers, found (wood shipping crates) or purchased (sawed-off whiskey barrels); in a half day or more of direct sun. Indoors, best herbs for winter production in pots are parsley, cilantro, dwarf bush basil, chives, rosemary, sweet bay.

Shrubs and Vines

During a period of unseasonably warm weather, several days or a week or so, watch for bud swellings on the twigs of spring-blooming shrubs and trees such as forsythia, flowering quince, flowering dogwood, flowering crab apple. Prune selectively, for the future wellness and appearance of the plant as well as to gain branches for coaxing into early bloom in vases.

IN BLOOM THIS MONTH

Winter jasmine. *Jasminum nudiflorum*. Bright yellow blossoms with green twigs, intermittently as the weather gives a few days of warm temperatures. Hardy to -10° F.

Wintersweet. *Chimonanthus praecox*. Deciduous shrub to shoulder height or taller, hardy to O° F. The flowers are ivory to creamy yellow, with red-brown centers; spicy fragrance. Plant in a winter sun pocket along a path where you will encounter it frequently. Clip a flowering twig for a bud vase by your bed.

Christmas rose. *Helleborus niger*. Evergreen perennial blooms in any moment of mild winter weather. The pink- to green- to burgundy-flushed white blossoms are as durable and resistant to the rigors of winter as they are beautiful. Be prepared to fall on your knees, however, to appreciate them, unless you have looked ahead to this moment and situated the plants in an upper garden so they can be admired at eye level.

William Sharp
(American, active 1819?-1862)
Fruit and Flower Piece, 1848
Oil on canvas, 36 x 29 inches
Bequest of Maxim Karolik
64.449

NEW PURCHASES

NEW PLANTINGS

NEW BLOOMINGS

Gustave Caillebotte
(French, 1848-1894)
Fruit Displayed on a Stand
Oil on canvas, 30⅛ x 39⅝ inches
Fanny P. Mason Fund in Memory of
Alice Thevin
1979.196

Welcome the Creation's Guest,
Lord of Earth and Heaven's Heir,
Lay aside that Warlike Crest,
And of Nature's banquets share:
Where the Souls of fruits and flow'rs
Stand prepar'd to heighten yours.

ANDREW MARVELL, "Pleasure"

1

HIGH

LOW

PREC.

2

HIGH

LOW

PREC.

3

HIGH

LOW

PREC.

4

HIGH

LOW

PREC.

And when the autumn winds have stript thee bare
And round thee lies the smooth, untrodden snow,
When naught is thine that made thee once so fair,
I love to watch thy shadowy form below,
And through thy leafless arms to look above
On stars that brighter shine when most
We need their love.

JONES VERY

5

HIGH

LOW

PREC.

George Hallowell
(American, 1871-1926)
Trees in Winter
Watercolor, 20 x 14½ inches
Gift of Frederick L. Jack
35.1234

Bouquet of Anemones, 1805
L.C. Ruotte, after J.L. Prevost (French, 1754-about 1806)
Stipple engraving, printed in color, 19¾ × 13 inches
Bequest of the Estate of George P. Dike, Elita R. Dike Collection
69.267

6

HIGH
LOW
PREC.

7

HIGH
LOW
PREC.

8

HIGH
LOW
PREC.

9

HIGH
LOW
PREC.

10

HIGH
LOW
PREC.

11

HIGH
LOW
PREC.

12

HIGH
LOW
PREC.

13

HIGH
LOW
PREC.

14

HIGH
LOW
PREC.

The infinite has written its name on the heavens in shining stars, and on the earth in tender flowers.

JEAN PAUL RICHTER

15

HIGH

LOW

PREC.

16

HIGH

LOW

PREC.

17

HIGH

LOW

PREC.

18

HIGH

LOW

PREC.

19

HIGH

LOW

PREC.

Mabel Julian
(American, 20th century)
Petunias, 1950
Watercolor, 16¼ x 22⅛ inches
Charles Henry Hayden Fund
for Provisional Watercolors
52.269

20

HIGH

LOW

PREC.

21

HIGH

LOW

PREC.

Pierre Auguste Renoir
(French, 1841-1919)
Mixed Flowers in an Earthenware Pot
Oil on paperboard mounted on canvas, 25½ x 21⅜ inches
Bequest of John T. Spaulding
48.592

22

HIGH

LOW

PREC.

23

HIGH

LOW

PREC.

24

HIGH

LOW

PREC.

25

HIGH

LOW

PREC.

26

HIGH

LOW

PREC.

Thus plants and flowers of the commonest kind can form a pleasing diary, because nothing which calls back to us the remembrance of a happy moment can be insignificant.

GOETHE, "Truth and Poetry"

27

HIGH

LOW

PREC.

28

HIGH

LOW

PREC.

29

HIGH

LOW

PREC.

30

HIGH

LOW

PREC.

31

HIGH

LOW

PREC.

Charles Emile Heil
(American, 1870-1950)
Snow Scene, 1916
Graphite & watercolor, 12⅛ × 11⅛ inches
Bequest of John T. Spaulding
48.797

Over the woodlands brown and bare
Over the harvest fields forsaken
Silent, and soft, and slow
Descends the snow

HENRY WADSWORTH LONGFELLOW,
"Snow-flakes"

FEBRUARY

GARDEN NOTES

Houseplants

Longer, hopeful days awaken resting roots and growth buds. Water more, begin regular applications of fertilizer — a blossom booster type such as 15-30-15 for flowering plants, a foliage or all-purpose fertilizer such as 23-21-17 for leafy types. Weeping fig, *Ficus benjamina*, will drop older leaves prematurely if it does not have adequate nitrogen when new leaves begin.

Start seeds in a warm, sunny window or fluorescent-light garden, especially kinds that aren't always available locally at planting time: Heliotrope, browallia, Tagetes lucida or pericon (a true marigold that tastes exactly like true French tarragon) and salpiglossis. Besides keeping seed plantings uniformly moist and constantly warm, at 70-75 F., success depends on this rule of (green) thumb: High light and relatively low temperatures produce short, stocky seedlings. Low light and relatively high temperatures produce tall, spindly seedlings.

Flowers

Organize incoming seeds, plants, bulbs, supplies.

Dejunk your garden storage facilities. The prospect can be daunting, but once you begin to organize all the pots by size, shape and material (plastic, clay, ceramic, other), then the seed trays and packs, the hoses, hoes and rakes — before you know it, things will be looking up. Call the American Horticultural Society's information database (1-800-777-7931) for guidance on whom to contact about the correct way to dispose of old, outmoded and outlawed garden pesticides.

Lawns

If you have a very large amount of lawn, consider the impact of converting part to the New American Garden (there is a public-access demonstration at the United States National Arboretum, Washington, D.C.) or Xeriscape (a concept introduced in the 1980s by the Denver Water Department and subsequently formalized and widely adopted). In either case the idea is not to set in motion any plantings that will require undue irrigation in normal times of drought; not to make plantings that require the use of environmentally damaging pesticides; to love, honor and obey nonrenewable resources. Visit a local garden center/nursery — a great spirit lifter for a bleak day when you think winter will never be over.

Edibles

Start seeds indoors of warm-season favorites: Tomato, eggplant, pepper. Jiffy 7 peat pots are time-savers: Soak the half-dollar-size pellet in warm water; after five minutes it becomes a self-contained pot. Sow three to five seeds in each. Try tomato varieties that commercial growers can't manage; there are all sizes and colors, from "true tomato" to pink, rose, white, yellow and striped.

Shrubs and Vines

In the deep South this is last call for pruning figs, other fruit trees and summer-flowering shrubs. Everywhere, remember not to prune the spring-flowering shrubs and vines until after they bloom — except for obviously dead branches, or the living ones you decide are expendable in the name of early bloom indoors, plunged deep in warm water and placed to develop in a bright spot. The cooler the average forcing temperatures, the slower the development of buds and the longer the life of the blossoms. Warmth speeds bloom, hastens its demise.

Roses

Be sure no one in a fit of late winter clean-up prunes back your once-yearly-blooming roses, the ramblers for example; wait until *after* bloom. Deep South: When the old roses start to bloom, it's last call for planting bare root roses this season.

There is always in February some one day, at least, when one smells the yet distant but surely coming summer.

GERTRUDE JEKYLL

Detail of illustration on page 101

IN BLOOM THIS MONTH

Corkscrew hazel or Harry Lauder's walking stick. *Corylus avellana 'Contorta.'* Deciduous shrub with twisting, turning branches that are best seen in winter, especially against new snow and when hung with the tassel-like catkins. (In some cases this needs protection from the resident flower arranger!)

Chinese witch-hazel. *Hamamelis mollis.* This deciduous shrub or small tree is one of the earliest to bloom, spidery yellow petals centered purplish-red, before the leaves. There are also numerous hybrids and cultivars; *H. x intermedia* 'Diana' has coppery red flowers. *H. vernalis.* hardy Zones 4–8, blooms at the merest hint of spring on the way.

Spring arrives any day in the Deep South, bringing with it great bouquets of bloom: azalea, bougainvillea, *Calycanthus floridus.* camellia, winter daphne, honeysuckle *(Lonicera fragrantissima. L. morrowii. L. tatarica).* jasmine, narcissus, Japanese flowering quince, scilla, snowdrop, snowflake, *Spiraea prunifolia. Spiraea thunbergi.* sweet olive and viburnum.

Sir Lawrence Alma-Tadema
(Dutch [worked in England],
1836-1912)
Woman and Flowers
(Opus LIX), 1868
Oil on panel, 19⅝ × 14⅝ inches
Gift of Edward Jackson Holmes
41.117

NEW PURCHASES

NEW PLANTINGS

2-22-94 - Garlic chives, chives (sprouted March 1)

NEW BLOOMINGS

1994 - Cyclamen Tricantha

Peter Blume
(American, born 1906)
Lilies, 1938
Gouache on paper, 15 x 22 inches
The Hayden Collection
41.264

Consider the lilies of the field, how they grow; they toil not, neither do they spin. And yet I say unto you, That even Solomon in all his glory was not arrayed like one of these.

ST. MATTHEW

Observe this dew-drenched rose of Tyrian gardens. A rose today. But you will ask in vain tomorrow what it is; and yesterday it was the dust, the sunshine, and the rain

LUCRETIUS

1

HIGH

LOW

PREC.

2

HIGH

LOW

PREC.

3

HIGH

LOW

PREC.

4

HIGH

LOW

PREC.

5

HIGH

LOW

PREC.

Mary Lawrance
(English, 1790-1831)
Rosa Provincialis/Rose de Rheims,
from a collection of *Roses from*
Nature, London, 1799
Soft ground etching and stipple
engraving, handcolored,
12⅞ × 11 inches
Bequest of the Estate of George P.
Dike, Elita R. Dike Collection 69.240

6

HIGH
LOW
PREC.

7

HIGH
LOW
PREC.

8

HIGH
LOW
PREC.

9

HIGH
LOW
PREC.

Man comes to build stately sooner than to garden finely, as if the latter were the greater perfection.
FRANCIS BACON, "On Gardening"

10

HIGH
LOW
PREC.

John Singer Sargent
(American, 1856-1925)
Florence: Boboli Gardens, about 1910
Watercolor on paper, 16 x 21 inches
Hayden Collection. Charles Henry
Hayden Fund
12.205

I I

HIGH

LOW

PREC.

I 2

HIGH

LOW

PREC.

Yet no — not words, for they
But half can tell love's feeling
Sweet flowers alone can say
What passion fears revealing.

THOMAS MOORE, "The Language of Flowers"

13

HIGH

LOW

PREC.

14

HIGH

LOW

PREC.

15

HIGH

LOW

PREC.

Marc Chagall
(Russian [worked in France],
1887-1985)
Village Street
Oil on canvas, 18⅛ × 15 inches
Bequest of Anna Feldberg
1978.156

16

HIGH
LOW
PREC.

17

HIGH
LOW
PREC.

18

HIGH
LOW
PREC.

19

HIGH
LOW
PREC.

20

HIGH
LOW
PREC.

21

HIGH

LOW

PREC.

22

1994-planted garlic chives + chives

HIGH

LOW

PREC.

23

HIGH

LOW

PREC.

24

HIGH

LOW

PREC.

Janet Fish (American, born 1948)
Spring Party, 1981
Oil on canvas, 55 x 31 inches
Collection of Mr. and Mrs. Graham Gund
Exhibited in *A Private Vision: Contemporary Art from the Graham Gund Collection*, 1982
Photography by Greg Heins

25

HIGH

LOW

PREC.

26

HIGH

LOW

PREC.

27

HIGH

LOW

PREC.

28

HIGH

LOW

PREC.

29

HIGH

LOW

PREC.

MARCH

GARDEN NOTES

Seeds
Almost anything can be started indoors now — tomatoes, peppers, eggplant and flowers you probably can't buy locally. St. Patrick's Day is the traditional time to plant sweet pea seeds outdoors in the North, presuming the ground can be worked or was prepared before winter freeze-up last autumn. Seeds of hardy annuals such as larkspur, cornflower and Iceland poppy can be sown in the garden where they are to grow. Gulf Coast gardeners can plant warm-season vegetables in place now: squash, tomatoes, peppers, eggplant.

Indoor gardening
Potted chrysanthemums and fuchsias can be encouraged into new growth by watering more freely and fertilizing lightly. Make tip cuttings of new shoots when they are four or five inches tall.

Bulbs, tubers
Start tuberous begonia, caladium and achimenes in flats or pots of peat moss and sand; keep moist and constantly warm. If caladium tubers are planted right side up, they produce fewer but larger leaves; if planted upside down they produce many more but smaller leaves. If you have a greenhouse, dahlia tubers may be potted up now, both for an early start and also to produce cuttings of choice sorts you'd like to increase. Deep South: Dahlias and cannas that have been left in the ground undisturbed several years will benefit from being dug and stored dry in a dark, cool place for four to six weeks, then divide and replant.

Flowers
As warm winds are felt, promising the arrival of spring in the near future, begin to take mulch away from border plants. This is so new soft growth doesn't commence under cover. Be cautious about pulling or digging out things that appear to have succumbed to winter; like people, some plants are naturally late risers.

Roses
Begin to remove winter mulches and covers, so that new growth naturally hardens to the fresh, cool air. Cut back large-flowered hybrids to about six inches if you want few but extra-large flowers; to twelve inches for more but smaller blossoms. Remove only obviously dead wood from climbers and ramblers, nothing more until after they bloom.

Shrubs
Don't prune any that bloom spring or early summer; wait until they finish flowering. Summer-flowering buddleias (but not the spring-flowering *Buddleia alternifolia*) and crape myrtles can be pruned now, at the gardener's convenience.

Trees, fruit
When new growth buds are just showing, but before the flowers begin to open, apply the first dormant spray. Follow container directions; be sure temperatures are above freezing, but cooler than 60° F. In the deep South, citrus and avocados can be planted, also papaya, banana, cherimoya. In the West, set out strawberry plants; pinch off first flowers to force energy toward establishing a strong root system.

Conifers, broadleaf evergreens
Plant or transplant before new growth becomes active. Water deeply early on, mulch later to stabilize soil temperature and moisture through hot weather.

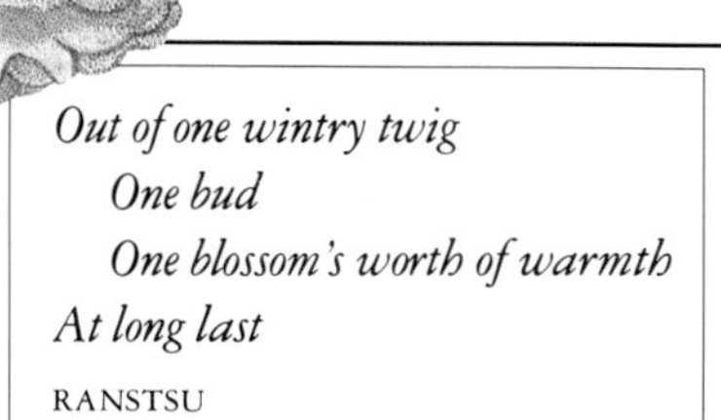

Out of one wintry twig
One bud
One blossom's worth of warmth
At long last

RANSTSU

Detail of illustration on page 63

Kingfisher on a flowering branch above water.
Qing Dynasty.
Shen Chuan
(Chinese, 1682-ca 1760)
Full color on silk, 10¼ × 7¾ inches
Helen S. Coolidge Fund
John Gardner Coolidge Collection
67.719

IN BLOOM THIS MONTH

Springwood white heath. *Erica carnea* 'Springwood.' This small-leaved evergreen groundcover shrublet has pendulous, creamy-white bells.

Buttercup winter-hazel, *Corylopsis pauciflora*, blooms early, even before the forsythias, and is hardy Zones 5–8. It has a graceful, arching habit and fragrant yellow bell flowers. (The branches are also delightful for forcing early indoors.) Ideal in light shade, at the edge of a woodland.

Forsythia comes in a range of yellows, from citron to golden, and in a variety of habits, from dwarf to very tall. 'Meadow Lark' is bud hardy to -35° F. 'Spring Glory' gives twice the number of flowers seen on ordinary forsythia. There is also a so-called white forsythia, *Abeliophyllum distichum*, a connoisseur plant from Korea with fragrant white blossoms. March-April, before the leaves.

Snowdrops, crocus, winter aconite: Little bulbs all, these harbingers of spring often put on a show even as banks of snow are melting into drifts of daffodils. Also blue *Irisreticulata* and golden *I. danfordiae*.

Spring is moving northward; azaleas and camellias are in full bloom in the deep South, also Carolina jasmine *(Gelsemium sempervirens)*, not to mention flowering almond, anemone, daphne, native iris, kerria, star magnolia, flowering peach, flowering pear, flowering quince, ranunculus, sweet olive and stock.

NEW PURCHASES

NEW PLANTINGS

NEW BLOOMINGS

Oscar Claude Monet
(French, 1840-1926)
Meadow with Poplars,
about 1875
Oil on canvas,
21½ x 25¾ inches
Bequest of David P. Kimball
in Memory of his wife, Clara
Bertram Kimball
23.505

I am never allowed to forget that a garden is an artificial contrivance imposed on nature. She does not tolerate this impertinence lightly.

WILLIAM LONGGOOD, *Voices from the Earth*

1

HIGH

LOW

PREC.

2

HIGH

LOW

PREC.

3

HIGH

LOW

PREC.

4

HIGH

LOW

PREC.

5

HIGH

LOW

PREC.

Nellie Littlehale Murphy
(American, 1867-1941)
Flower Study
Watercolor, 22 × 28 inches
Painting Department Special Fund
28.52

6

HIGH

LOW

PREC.

7

HIGH

LOW

PREC.

8

HIGH

LOW

PREC.

9

HIGH

LOW

PREC.

Frederic Crowninshield
(American, 1845-1918)
Spring Blossoms, 1882
Watercolor, 14½ × 20½ inches
Gift of Mrs. Frederick J. Bradlee, Jr.
45.44

10

HIGH

LOW

PREC.

11

HIGH

LOW

PREC.

12

HIGH

LOW

PREC.

We complain and complain, but we have lived and seen the blossoms — apple, pear, cherry, plum, almond blossoms — in the sun; and the best among us cannot pretend they deserve — or could contrive — anything better.

J.B. PRIESTLEY, "Delight"

13

HIGH

LOW

PREC.

Maurice Brazil Prendergast
(American, 1859-1924)
Flowers in a Blue Vase,
about 1915
Oil on canvas, 19 × 16 inches
Bequest of John T. Spaulding
48.589

14

HIGH

LOW

PREC.

15

HIGH

LOW

PREC.

16

HIGH

LOW

PREC.

17

HIGH

LOW

PREC.

18

HIGH

LOW

PREC.

19

HIGH

LOW

PREC.

Rhodora! if the sages ask thee why
This charm is wasted on the earth and sky,
Tell them, dear, that if eyes were made for seeing,
Then Beauty is its own excuse for being.
RALPH WALDO EMERSON, "The Rhodora"

20

HIGH
LOW
PREC.

21

HIGH
LOW
PREC.

22

HIGH
LOW
PREC.

23

HIGH
LOW
PREC.

24

HIGH
LOW
PREC.

25

HIGH

LOW

PREC.

26

HIGH

LOW

PREC.

27

HIGH

LOW

PREC.

Samuel Holden
(English, active about 1834-1849)
Rondeletia Longiflora
Hand-colored lithograph from
Joseph Paxton, *Magazine of Botany and Register of Flowering Plants* (London, 1834-1849), 9⅛ × 6¼ inches
Bequest of Estate of George P. Dike
69.337

Nobody sees a flower — really — it is so small — we haven't time — and to see takes time like to have a friend takes time.

GEORGIA O'KEEFFE

28

HIGH

LOW

PREC.

29

HIGH

LOW

PREC.

30

HIGH

LOW

PREC.

31

HIGH

LOW

PREC.

Georgia O'Keeffe
(American, 1887-1986)
White Rose with Larkspur No. 2, 1927
Oil on canvas, 40 × 30 inches
Henry H. and Zoë Oliver Sherman Fund
Courtesy of the Estate of Georgia O'Keeffe
1980.207

APRIL

GARDEN NOTES

Houseplants

Top priority at this season usually goes to outdoor gardening. A few minutes of quality time spent daily on the indoor plant population can do wonders. If you get rained in, don't fret. There are lots of gardening chores that can be done inside or at night. Grooming and repotting houseplants. Writing out labels for outdoor plantings. Organizing orders and catalogs so the information you need will be accessible on a moment's notice.

Flowers

For indoor or outdoor pots come warm weather, invest now in achimenes, flowering gingers such as *Kaempferia pulchra*, pineapple lily *(Eucomis undulata)*, florist gloxinia, haemanthus, tuberous begonia and caladium. All grow from some kind of bulb or bulblike storehouse and bloom generously when the days are long, the air lifted by balmy breezes. Achimenes and gloxinias are ideal porch plants.

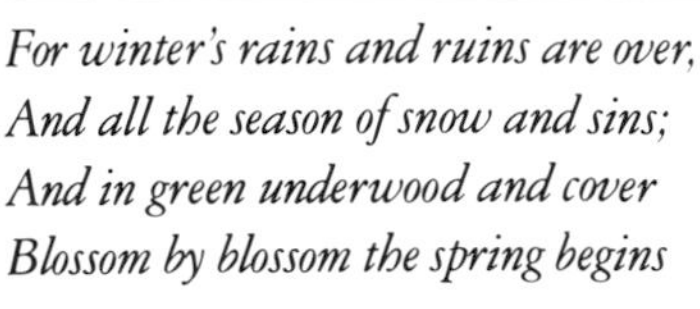

For winter's rains and ruins are over,
And all the season of snow and sins;
And in green underwood and cover
Blossom by blossom the spring begins

ALGERNON CHARLES SWINBURNE, "Atlanta in Calydon"

Detail of illustration on page 101

Flower borders

Clean out the dead, evict the weeds. See what you have left. Winter may have taken its toll, not to mention dry or wet disasters beyond your control. Assess the damage. Consider the possibilities. Since most gardeners want to grow more than they will ever have space for, spring vacancies are more to be welcomed than mourned. More and more local garden centers are stocking a fascinating array of ornamental grasses.

Trees

If you've been longing to plant one or more trees, do so as soon as frost is out of the ground, the earlier in the season the better. Of all the things we plant, trees take the longest to mature. There is a very brief time in early spring when trees can be transplanted bare-root. Transplanting from containers or with a ball of earth about the roots is feasible over a much longer period. Prepare the soil well and incorporate some compost. But don't overdo on the hole, or it may act more as a container than as a place where the tree can send its roots deeply into the endemic soil and thus before more self-reliant.

Some trees and shrubs do best if transplanted in the spring. These include birch, magnolia, tulip tree, sweet gum, Japanese maple, large-flowering dogwood, althea, flowering almond, ornamental cherry, peach, buddleia, hawthorn, rhododendron and weigela.

Last call for pruning grapevines and orchard fruits. Trim box and privet hedges before they start into growth. Evergreens in need of thickening and shaping can be sheared to advantage as new growth is commencing.

Edibles

In cold regions start individual pots inside for such warm-season vegetables as beans, eggplant, okra, pepper, tomato and sweet corn. (Insider's tip: Soak okra seeds in household bleach one hour before planting; they'll sprout much more quickly, with more enthusiasm.) Harvest from early indoor sowings can come in as much as a month earlier than those planted directly in the garden. Sow herbs in open border spots: thyme, dill, sage, marjoram, chives, oregano.

Roses

In coldest regions wait until the new growth buds are about to appear and then prune large-flowered hybrids to three eyes or four to six inches of wood. Pruning of roses is largely to develop new wood and to direct growth so that the plant is open toward the middle of the bush. If you plant any roses bare-root, a few inches of soil or compost heaped over the crown will help keep canes from drying out until roots take hold; after a couple of weeks, use your fingers carefully to pull down the small mounds.

IN BLOOM THIS MONTH

Ajuga. Azalea. Basket-of-gold alyssum *(Aurinia saxatile)*. Candytuft. Columbine. Daffodil. Dogwood. Flowering almond. Flowering cherry. Flowering peach. Flowering quince. Forget-me-not. Hyacinth. Iris. Jacob's ladder. Lily-of-the-valley. Pansy. *Phlox divaricata. P. subulata.* Primrose. Ranunculus. Redbud. Scilla. Shooting star. Tulip. Vinca. Violet.

Phlox divaricata, known variously as wild sweet William, blue phlox and Louisiana phlox, grows wild from Quebec to Michigan and south to Georgia and northern Alabama. Color varies from pale violet-blue to lavender. There is also 'Alba' (white), 'Grandiflora' (larger flowers than the species), 'Laphamii' (large, intense blue-violet). Preferred colors found in garden plantings may be propagated by division of the spreading root systems.

The Stellar dogwoods, developed at Rutgers University by Dr. Elwin Orton, represent the mating of native dogwood, *Cornus florida*, with the Asian *C. kousa*. The progeny are better all around — more flowers, stronger habit, and greater disease resistance.

Lilian Westcott Hale
(American, 1881-1963)
L'Edition de Luxe, 1910
Oil on canvas, 23¼ x 15 inches
Gift of Miss Mary C. Wheelwright
35.1487

NEW PURCHASES

NEW PLANTINGS

NEW BLOOMINGS

Oscar Claude Monet
(French, 1840-1926)
Morning on the Seine, near Giverny, 1896
Oil on canvas, 29 × 36⅝ inches
Juliana Cheney Edwards Collection
39.655

A Little Madness in the Spring
Is wholesome even for the King
But God be with the Clown
Who ponders this tremendous scene—
This whole experiment of Green
As if it were his own!
EMILY DICKINSON, "#1333"

1

HIGH

LOW

PREC.

2

HIGH

LOW

PREC.

George Morren
(Belgian, 1868-1941)
Garden Wall, 1892
Oil on canvas,
21¼ x 26⅜ inches
Deposited by the Trustees
of the White Fund,
Lawrence, Massachusetts
1326.12

3

HIGH
LOW
PREC.

4

HIGH
LOW
PREC.

5

HIGH
LOW
PREC.

6

HIGH
LOW
PREC.

A garden is like those pernicious machineries which catch a man's coat-skirt, or his hand, and draw in his leg and his whole body to irresistible destruction.

RALPH WALDO EMERSON, "Conduct of Life"

7

HIGH

LOW

PREC.

8

HIGH

LOW

PREC.

9

HIGH

LOW

PREC.

10 Frost Free Date

HIGH

LOW

PREC.

11

HIGH

LOW

PREC.

Langlois (active 1805-1840),
after P.J. Redouté
Lilacs, 1827
Stipple Engraving printed
in color and handcolored,
8¼ x 10¾ inches
Bequest of the Estate
of George P. Dike,
Elita R. Dike Collection
69.281

12

HIGH

LOW

PREC.

13

HIGH

LOW

PREC.

Lilas.

P. J. Redouté. — 73. Langlois.

April is the cruellest month, breeding
Lilacs out of the dead land, mixing
Memory and desire, stirring
Dull roots with spring rain.
T.S. ELIOT, "The Waste Land"

14

HIGH

LOW

PREC.

15

HIGH

LOW

PREC.

16

HIGH

LOW

PREC.

17

HIGH

LOW

PREC.

18

HIGH

LOW

PREC.

19

HIGH

LOW

PREC.

20

HIGH

LOW

PREC.

John Joseph Enneking
(American, 1841-1916)
Spring Hillside, 1899-1902
Oil on canvas, 24½ × 34½ inches
Gift of the Heirs of George Adams
Kettell 13.474

21

HIGH

LOW

PREC.

22

HIGH

LOW

PREC.

23

HIGH

LOW

PREC.

24

HIGH

LOW

PREC.

25

HIGH

LOW

PREC.

26

HIGH

LOW

PREC.

After J.L. Prevost
(French, 1760-1810)
Bouquet of Yellow and White Roses, Hyacynths, and Narcissus,
from *Collection des Fleurs et des Fruits,*
Book 4, Plate 16
Stipple engraving, printed in color and handcolored,
19⅜ × 12⅝ inches
Bequest of the Estate of George P. Dike,
Elita R. Dike Collection
69.264

27

HIGH
LOW
PREC.

28

HIGH
LOW
PREC.

29

HIGH
LOW
PREC.

30

HIGH
LOW
PREC.

If I had but two loaves of bread, I would sell one and buy hyacinths, for they would feed my soul.

THE KORAN

MAY

GARDEN NOTES

Edibles, flowers, any seed you are sowing directly where it is to grow
The more care you exercise in sowing thinly, the less time you will have to spend later in thinning. Crowded seedlings don't do as well as those with enough room to flex and grow. Thinnings of baby lettuce, cabbage, radishes, tiny onions make crunchy additions to green salads. By the end of the month everything can be planted outdoors, sweet and popping corn, pole, snap and lima beans.

Flowers
As early bloomers finish — creeping phlox, woods phlox, primroses, violets — it is a good time to do any lifting, dividing and replanting that may need doing, usually every third year.

Houseplants
Round up all those holiday celebrants and decide which ones to keep and which to compost. Poinsettias, if cut back by half or more and repotted, can become beautiful foliage plants; getting them to rebloom as fully as the professionals do is not easy. Cyclamen grows from a tuber that needs a time of dryness in summer, to the point of shriveling the leaves and discouraging further active growth. Keep at around 60-70° F. in a dry, dark place. Start watering again in late summer. Christmas and other holiday cacti need warmth, water and fertilizer in spring and summer, with fairly strong sun to boost growth and harden them sufficiently to flower freely. Cut back kalanchoe and root tip cuttings for more plants. Azaleas can be planted outdoors if of a hardy type; otherwise, repot now, to a size or two larger pot, and fill in with moist sphagnum peat moss.

Vines
In southern California and other warmer reaches of the Sun Belt, now is the time to prune winter-flowering vines.

Bulbs
Northern gardeners can make the first planting of gladiolus corms, for blooms in about two months. Plant successionally every two or three weeks to extend the flowering season. Not all gladiolus are big ugly stalks with half-withered flowers in insipid or unsafe-at-any-speed colors. There are some beauties among the species and the miniature glads.

Flowers
Christmas and Lenten roses, *Helleborus*, can be transplanted if necessary when flowering finishes. It's best to site with sensitivty to their needs, since they move with reluctance. Part shade. Humus-rich, well-drained soil. No severe or protracted droughts; mulching with organic matter can help solve this if it should be a problem. Scatter 5-10-5 or similar balanced, all-purpose fertilizer over soil about to be prepared for planting. Also side-dress around established perennial flowers; those that will be blooming in the summer, such as *Phlox paniculata*, and in the fall, such as aster and chrysanthemum, will benefit from another side-dressing later on.

Peonies
If botrytis blight has been a problem in your garden, spray the emerging shoots of herbaceous peonies with a fungicide. Don't fret if ants are on the buds: they are only after the honey. Disbudding results in fewer, larger flowers. Remove lesser buds with your fingers as soon as they are large enough that you can discern one from the other.

Shrubs
Prune the early shrubs such as forsythia and lilac as soon as they finish flowering. Remove to the ground some of the oldest canes or stems whether or not they produced blooms this year. This is the way to build a strong, open shrub that blooms abundantly year after year.

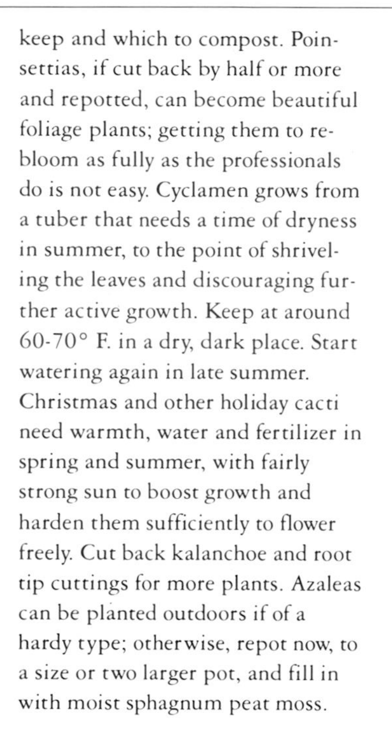

Hail, bounteous May, that dost inspire
Mirth and youth and warm desire
Woods and groves are of thy dressing
Hill and dale doth boast thy blessing.
Thus we salute thee with our early song
And welcome thee and wish thee long.
JOHN MILTON, "Song: On May Morning"

Detail of illustration on page 18

IN BLOOM THIS MONTH

A shorter list would be what is not in bloom at the high tide of spring; here are some of the most memorable: Abelia. Azalea. English bluebells. Bluebonnet. Bougainvillea. *Buddleia alternifolia.* Indian hawthorn. Irises, many, including tall bearded or German, Siberian and Spuria. Mountain laurel *(Kalmia).* Kerria. Beauty bush *(Kolkwitzia).* Lilac. Mock orange. Poet's narcissus. Peonies. Early old-fashioned and climbing roses such as 'Lady Banks'. Spirea. Late tulips. Wisteria.

Beauty bush, *Kolkwitzia amabilis,* hardy Zones 4–8, will adapt even in sandy, dry situations. The cultivar 'Pink Cloud' is particularly gardenworthy. It was raised at the Royal Horticultural Society Garden at Wisley, England, from seeds obtained from the Morton Arboretum, Lisle, Illinois. Promote beauty bush flower production by cutting back oldest stems to the ground each year after bloom finishes.

Laura Coombs Hills
(American, 1859-1952)
Larkspur, Peonies, and Canterbury Bells, about 1915
Pastel on paper, 28 × 23¼ inches
Purchased from the Ellen Kelleran Gardner Picture Fund 26.240

NEW PURCHASES

NEW PLANTINGS

NEW BLOOMINGS

John La Farge
(American, 1835-1910)
Apple Blossoms,
about 1879
Watercolor on paper, 7 x 9½ inches
Bequest of Mrs. Henry Lee Higginson
35.1175

Nature will bear the closest inspection.
She invites us to lay our eye level with her smallest
leaf and take an insect view of it plain.

HENRY DAVID THOREAU, *Journals*

I

HIGH

LOW

PREC.

May 1. At last the Garden of Dreams has awakened. It is! After the healthful winter of snow the whole land is a-bloom . . . Is it not all my garden? All the cultivated and the wild, every flower and fern in the wood and open as well, for not only what I plant is mine, but also everything that I enjoy.

MABEL OSGOOD WRIGHT

2

HIGH

LOW

PREC.

3

HIGH

LOW

PREC.

William McGregor Paxton
(American, 1869-1941)
Betty in the Garden, about 1930
Oil on canvas, 20¼" x 25⅛"
Bequest of Marian E. Phipps
1987.549

4

HIGH

LOW

PREC.

PAXTON

5

HIGH

LOW

PREC.

6

HIGH

LOW

PREC.

7

HIGH

LOW

PREC.

8

HIGH

LOW

PREC.

9

HIGH

LOW

PREC.

10

HIGH

LOW

PREC.

11

HIGH

LOW

PREC.

Nelly Littlehale Murphy
(American, 1867-1941)
Peonies, 1937
Watercolor on paper,
22¾ x 22¾ inches
Gift of H. Dudley Murphy
in memory of the artist
42.191

12

HIGH

LOW

PREC.

13

HIGH

LOW

PREC.

John Appleton Brown
(American, 1844-1902)
A Showery May Morning,
about 1890-1900
Oil on canvas, 31 x 42 inches
Bequest of Charles T. and
Susan P. Baker
21.1254

14

HIGH
LOW
PREC.

15

HIGH
LOW
PREC.

16

HIGH
LOW
PREC.

17

HIGH
LOW
PREC.

18

HIGH
LOW
PREC.

19

HIGH

LOW

PREC.

20

HIGH

LOW

PREC.

21

HIGH

LOW

PREC.

22

HIGH

LOW

PREC.

23

HIGH

LOW

PREC.

24

HIGH

LOW

PREC.

Another May, new buds and flowers shall bring
Ah, why has happiness no second spring?
CHARLOTTE SMITH, "Elegiac Sonnets"

25

HIGH

LOW

PREC.

Léon Hartl
(American, 1889-1967)
Still Life, 1953
Watercolor, 22¾ × 31 inches
Gift of the William H. Lane Foundation
1990.411

26

HIGH

LOW

PREC.

27

HIGH

LOW

PREC.

28

HIGH

LOW

PREC.

29

HIGH

LOW

PREC.

30

HIGH

LOW

PREC.

31

HIGH

LOW

PREC.

Flowers are restful to look at.
They have neither
emotions nor conflicts.
SIGMUND FREUD

Narcisse Virgile Diaz de la Peña
(French, 1808-1876)
Flowers
Oil on canvas, 15¾ × 9⅞ inches
Bequest of Ellen F. Moseley through
Margaret LeMoyne Wentworth and
Helen Freeman Hull 24.236

JUNE

GARDEN NOTES

Houseplants
As heat outdoors increases, air circulation and shading is all the more critical for the welfare of indoor plants, especially those in sun rooms or home conservatories of any type. When air conditioning is required, take care that cold drafts from it do not blow directly on tropical plants.

Container plantings outdoors
During hottest weather, twice-daily watering may be needed. This rapidly leaches out the nutrients; offset by watering once weekly with fertilizer diluted to half the usual strength every two weeks. Weekly fertilizing keeps growth constant and strong. An alternative is to topdress with timed-release fertilizer pellets. These last a season and automatically give some nutrients to the plant roots with every watering. In extremely hot weather, overheating of the soil in outdoor containers can have a deleterious effect on the inhabitants even when they are well-watered and fertilized. Unglazed clay and terra-cotta pots permit moisture to evaporate through the walls, which has a beneficial cooling effect. It is also important to boost containers on one- to two-inch blocks of wood or bricks so that air can circulate freely under them.

Trees, shrubs
In the absence of rain, water slowly, deeply, infrequently; avoid rapid, quick irrigation methods that compact the soil, lead to soil erosion and do not sink in but rather run off and may contribute to various environmental problems. A drip irrigation system works most efficiently for home orchards, food gardens and all kinds of so-called ornamentals such as shade and flowering trees, flowering and fruiting shrubs, flowers and vines. Mulching with organic matter is a primary step to take as soon as spring planting and cultivating are in hand. A layer up to three or four inches deep will prevent excessive weed invasion, preserve soil moisture and stabilize soil temperatures.

Flowers
Permit the leaves of tulips, daffodils *(Narcissus)*, hyacinths and other spring-blooming bulbs to ripen before removing them. This means not mowing over meadows where bulbs are naturalized until the leaves start to turn yellow.

Edibles
Cultivation of the surface soil is extremely important at this time. It creates a dust mulch that is surprisingly effective against excessive drying and serves to remove weed seedlings as they are emerging, before their roots become stubbornly established. The harder a weed becomes to evict, the more it is robbing the soil of moisture and nutrients needed by the desired crop.

Woodland and wildflower gardens
Early summer is an ideal time to add an acidic mulch, to preserve moisture and to keep the roots of acid-loving plants adequately supplied, kinds such as azalea and rhododendron, mountain laurel and highbush blueberry. Well-rotted oak leaves or pine needles are excellent in this situation.

The roses make the world so sweet,
The bees, the birds have such a tune
There's such a light and such a heat
And such a joy in June.
GEORGE MACDONALD, "To ______________ "

Ignace Henry Jean Théodore
Fantin-Latour (French, 1836-1904)
Roses in a Glass Vase, 1890
Oil on canvas, 16¾ x 14⅞ inches
Bequest of Alice A. Hay
1987.291

IN BLOOM THIS MONTH

Roses. Delphiniums. Shasta daisies. Madonna and other lilies. Lavender hedges. Bedding geraniums. Mock-orange. Abelia. Achillea. Agapanthus. Bedding begonia. Buttonbush. Caladium. *Centranthus ruber* or red valerian. Clematis. Crinum. Daylily, or *Hemerocallis.* Forget-me-not. True *Geranium* species, varieties and cultivars. Honeysuckle. Hydrangea. Iris. Lantana. Larkspur. Nasturtium. Oleander. Passionflower. Petunia. Pinks. Snapdragon. Spirea. Yucca.

Since the roses that bloom only once a year are mostly out in June, along with those that will bloom intermittently all season, this is the time to be out looking and smelling, comparing and making lists of which ones you'd like where in future plantings. There is a trend toward placing together all the newer hybrid teas and grandifloras, in one class of large-flowered hybrids. The floribundas and other smaller-and cluster-flowered roses are coming into their own as landscape plants. When roses are planted in a formal garden, we tend to think of them as high-maintenance plants, yet they can also be deployed as sensible, beautiful ground cover.

In common with clematis, delphiniums need cool, moist soil, but their top parts need lots of sun. It is also well to space the plants so that air can circulate freely.

NEW PURCHASES

NEW PLANTINGS

NEW BLOOMINGS

Ross Sterling Turner
(American, 1847-1915)
A Garden is a Sea of Flowers, 1912
Watercolor on paper,
20½ x 30½ inches
Gift of the Estate of Nellie P. Carter
35.1690

What is one to say about June — the time of perfect young summer, the fulfillment of the promise of the earlier months, and with as yet no sign to remind one that its fresh young beauty will ever fade? For my own part, I wander up into the wood and say, "June is here — June is here; thank God for lovely June."

GERTRUDE JEKYLL

Eugene Speicher
(American, 1883-1962)
Bouquet, about 1925
Oil on canvas,
16½ × 14¼ inches
Bequest of John T. Spaulding
48.602

1

HIGH
LOW
PREC.

2

HIGH
LOW
PREC.

3

HIGH
LOW
PREC.

4

HIGH
LOW
PREC.

5

HIGH
LOW
PREC.

6

HIGH
LOW
PREC.

7

HIGH

LOW

PREC.

8

HIGH

LOW

PREC.

9

HIGH

LOW

PREC.

10

HIGH

LOW

PREC.

John La Farge
(American, 1835-1910)
Bowl of Wild Roses, 1880
Watercolor on paper,
8½ × 7½ inches
Bequest of Miss Elizabeth Howard Bartol
Res. 27.96

11

HIGH

LOW

PREC.

12

HIGH

LOW

PREC.

13

HIGH

LOW

PREC.

14

HIGH

LOW

PREC.

15

HIGH

LOW

PREC.

16

HIGH

LOW

PREC.

17

HIGH

LOW

PREC.

Accuse not Nature! She hath done her part.
Do thou but thine.

JOHN MILTON, *Paradise Lost*

18

HIGH

LOW

PREC.

Oscar Claude Monet
(French, 1840-1926)
Poppy Field in a Hollow near Giverny, 1885
Oil on canvas, 25¾ x 32 inches
Juliana Cheney Edwards Collection
25.106

19

HIGH

LOW

PREC.

To own a bit of ground, to scratch it with a hoe, to plant seeds and watch their renewal of life — this is the commonest delight of the race, the most satisfactory thing one can do.

CHARLES DUDLEY WARNER

20

HIGH

LOW

PREC.

21

HIGH

LOW

PREC.

22

HIGH

LOW

PREC.

Albert André (French, 1869-1954)
Petunias, 1893
Gouache on paperboard mounted on panel, 19¼ x 25¾ inches
Anonymous Gift
38.777

23

HIGH

LOW

PREC.

24

HIGH

LOW

PREC.

25

HIGH

LOW

PREC.

26

HIGH

LOW

PREC.

27

HIGH

LOW

PREC.

28

HIGH

LOW

PREC.

29

HIGH

LOW

PREC.

30

HIGH

LOW

PREC.

Mary Stevenson Cassatt
(American, 1844-1926)
Gathering Fruit, about 1893
Drypoint, softground etching, and aquatint in color (9th state)
16⅝ × 11¾ inches
Gift of William Emerson and Charles Henry Hayden Fund
41.813

JULY

GARDEN NOTES

Lawns

Mow higher in hottest weather, so that no more than an inch or an amount equal to a third of the total height of the grass is cut at one clipping. This makes life easier for the grass plant at a time when nature is likely to stress it and helps it overgrow and shade out weeds. If you wish to water your lawn during a period of drought, follow any local restrictions as to time and frequency. The equivalent of an inch of rain weekly works well on most lawns and is best applied in one, long, slow gentle soak, versus several short and quick showers.

In beastly hot, dry weather, try not to walk repeatedly across the lawn, as this easily causes permanent damage. Mowing can be put off until a soaking rain and a little cooler weather have given the grass a chance to grow enough to merit a light clipping.

> *Now it is summer, and as usual, life fills me with transport and I forget to work. This year I have struggled for a long time, but the beauty of the world has conquered me.*
>
> RALPH WALDO EMERSON

Roses

After the once-a-year-blooming climbers and ramblers finish flowering, remove the oldest, bloomed-out trunks or stems, right down to the ground. Cut off old lateral branches to a main promising cane. This boosts vigorous new shoots which, when tied into a semi-horizontal position, will break laterals all along their length, on which next year's blooms will appear. Roses of this type can be increased by layering: Bend a long cane to the ground and cover the end with moist soil. If needed, apply a stone or clothespin where it will do the most good in holding the layer in place. The new plant should have rooted by next spring and be ready at that time to be severed from the parent and transplanted to a permanent position.

Flowers

As the early perennials finish blooming, deadhead any that appear tattered, especially delphinium, Shasta daisy, coreopsis, achillea and foxglove, or digitalis. This helps the garden look more appealing, and a deft and well-timed snip here and there will result in more blooms later in the season.

After the rush of spring gardening there is often a lull beginning around the Fourth of July. If you need more perennial flowers, now could be the time to plant seeds. The seedbed will need protection from hottest sun and a constant supply of moisture. Seedlings will be large enough by fall to plant into the border; in coldest North, carry seedlings over winter in a frame, and wait until spring to transplant.

Don't prune or cut back chrysanthemums or poinsettias after about July 15. This is to be sure there is time for the wood to form on which flowers can be produced this coming fall and early winter.

Edibles

Pull out any remaining early lettuce or radishes before they go to seed. Plant a warm-weather crop in their place, such as bush green beans or black-eyed peas. Sow more rows of sweet corn every ten days to two weeks. Blocks of several short rows together work better than one or two long rows; this has to do with pollination, which is everything when it comes to a crop cultivated for its seeds.

Remember to put on the compost pile all the vegetable matter waste from your kitchen. This means that potato and carrot peelings, celery trimmings top and bottom and all matter of discarded leaves, pulp and fiber can contribute to the compost and not be wasted down the kitchen disposal unit.

Odilon Redon (French, 1840-1916)
Large Green Vase with Mixed Flowers
Pastel on paper, 29¼ × 24½ inches
Bequest of John T. Spaulding
48.591

IN BLOOM THIS MONTH

Rose-of-Sharon or shrub althea *(Hibiscus syriacus)*. summer-blooming tamarisk *(Tamarix* 'Pink Cascade' and *T.* '*Summer Glow*'). Japanese pagoda tree or Chinese scholar tree *(Sophora japonica)*. Buttonbush *(Cephalanthus occidentalis)*. Chinese parasol tree *(Firmiana simplex)*. Goldenrain tree *(Koelreuteria paniculata)*. Also abelia, achimenes, ageratum, balloon-flower (*platycodon*), scarlet runner bean, blackberry lily (*belamcanda*), butterfly bush (*buddleia*), canna, cleome, coneflower (*echinacea*), cosmos, dahlia, datura, daylily (*hemerocallis*), four o'clock (*mirabilis*), gladiolus, hollyhock, impatiens, lantana, lythrum, marigold, moonflower, morning glory, oleander, passionflower, periwinkle, petunia, portulaca, roses, sunflower, tigridia, flowering tobacco, trumpet creeper, verbena, veronica, water lily and zinnia.

Rose-of-Sharon, *Hibiscus syriacus*. is an old-fashioned summer-flowering shrub that has been somewhat maligned by the gardening establishment owing to the promotion of a "patriotic" rose-of-Sharon plant on which are grafted the three colors red, white and blue. This apparent vulgarity needn't keep the clear-headed gardener from planting any of the improved cultivars and training them as either bushes or tree-form standards. In any case, spring pruning is essential, back by as much as a third or more, since flowering occurs each year on new wood formed in the same season.

NEW PURCHASES

NEW PLANTINGS

NEW BLOOMINGS

Henri Matisse (French 1869-1954)
Vase of Flowers, 1916
Oil on canvas, 23⅞ x 29 inches
Bequest of John T. Spaulding,
48.577

I never had any other desire so strong and so like to covetousness as that one which I have always had that I might be master at last of a small house and a large garden.

ABRAHAM COWLEY, "The Garden"

1

HIGH

LOW

PREC.

2

HIGH

LOW

PREC.

3

HIGH

LOW

PREC.

4

HIGH

LOW

PREC.

How does the meadowflower its bloom unfold?
Because the lovely little flower is free
Down to its root, and in that freedom bold.

WILLIAM WORDSWORTH

5

HIGH

LOW

PREC.

Polly Nordell
(American, 1876-1956)
Wildflowers
Watercolor, 20⅜ × 14¾ inches
Gift of Eunice E. Huntsman
1981.60

6

HIGH

LOW

PREC.

7

HIGH

LOW

PREC.

8

HIGH

LOW

PREC.

9

HIGH

LOW

PREC.

10

HIGH

LOW

PREC.

11

HIGH

LOW

PREC.

12

HIGH

LOW

PREC.

13

HIGH

LOW

PREC.

14

HIGH

LOW

PREC.

15

HIGH

LOW

PREC.

16

HIGH

LOW

PREC.

Oscar Claude Monet
(French, 1840-1926)
Camille Monet and a Child in the Artist's Garden in Argenteuil, 1875
Oil on canvas, 21¾ x 25½ inches
Anonymous Gift in Memory of
Mr. and Mrs. Edwin S. Webster
1976.833

17

HIGH

LOW

PREC.

18

HIGH

LOW

PREC.

19

HIGH

LOW

PREC.

20

HIGH

LOW

PREC.

21

HIGH

LOW

PREC.

Attributed to J. June
(English, about 1740-1770)
Basket of Flowers Including London Pride, Carnations and Ten Others, with Beetle on Table, 1755
Probably from T. Bowles,
Four Arrangements in Baskets, 1755
Etching and engraving, handcolored,
16 × 20 inches
Bequest of the Estate of George P. Dike,
Elita R. Dike Collection
69.219

22

HIGH

LOW

PREC.

23

HIGH

LOW

PREC.

24

HIGH

LOW

PREC.

25

HIGH

LOW

PREC.

26

HIGH

LOW

PREC.

27

HIGH

LOW

PREC.

28

HIGH

LOW

PREC.

When we plant a tree, we are doing what we can to make our planet a more wholesome and happier dwelling place for those that come after us, if not for ourselves.

OLIVER WENDELL HOLMES

29

HIGH

LOW

PREC.

30

HIGH

LOW

PREC.

31

HIGH

LOW

PREC.

John William Hill
(American, 1812-1879)
Study of Fruit, 1877
Watercolor, 6⅛ x 10⅝ inches
M. and M. Karolik Collection
55.753

AUGUST

GARDEN NOTES

Trees
New growth has hardened on evergreens, so light trimming can be safely done. Use the clippings as mulch or for making compost. Be sure to shape hedges so that they are wider at the bottom, more narrow toward the top. This is to encourage fullness to the ground rather than the usual thinning-out at the base.

Herbs
Harvest leafy herbs as they are coming into flower — kinds such as dill, sweet basil and mint. Wash leaves very lightly, briefly in cool water, then spread on trays to dry or hang in a cool, dry, dust-free place. Containerize and label the leaves as soon as they are fully dry. Wait to break up the individual leaves until you are about to add them to a recipe. This preserves the essential oils.

That delicate forest flower,
With scented breath and look so like a smile
Seems, as it issues from the shapeless mould
An emanation of the indwelling Life,
A visible token of the upholding Love,
That are the soul of this great universe.

WILLIAM CULLEN BRYANT, "A Forest Hymn"

Flowers
Herbaceous peonies can be ordered now for planting in a few weeks. Established clumps can be dug and divided when the worst of summer heat is over. Peonies may not bloom if they are shaded out by encroaching trees, shrubs or weeds. Peony roots must be set so that the growth eyes are precisely one to two inches deep, no more, no less; otherwise, they will not bloom properly. When summer phlox finish flowering, cut off the spent flower heads immediately, before seeds form. This channels energy to the roots and also prevents self-sown seedlings which revert to insipid colors and exhibit aggressive behavior toward the desirable phlox cultivars. Disbud dahlias and chrysanthemums for fewer, larger blossoms.
Prepare seedbeds in frames or in small pockets throughout the border or cottage garden where the seeds are to grow. Plant seeds of foxglove, hollyhock, pansy, delphinium, platycodon and lupine. Lupines in particular are best sown where they are to grow; their roots react badly to disturbance.

Roses
Roses can be fertilized now in the warmer regions of the country where flowering continues until near the end of the year. Elsewhere it is probably too late, as fertilizer now could encourage new growth that will not have time to harden before killing frosts.

Lawns
If moss seems to be taking over, it is a sign the soil is very acidic. It may also be a welcome sign, that you should encourage a moss lawn instead of struggling to have a grass one. Moss lawns are much admired in Japan and the idea is increasingly appealing in North America.

Bulbs
Order spring-flowering types such as tulips, daffodils and hyacinths for planting out this fall. Try some of the autumn-flowering crocus, colchicum and sternbergia. They are hardy bulbs that bloom in autumn and give the gardener an unexpected lift. August is the time to plant bulbs of the madonna lily, *Lilium candidum*.

Edibles
Cut and plant strawberry runners now, to assure strong-producing young plants next season and outstanding harvest in two years. Remove any raspberry and blackberry canes that have finished bearing. Wait to prune this year's new canes until next spring, unless they grow entirely too tall, in which case cutting back to five feet is permissible. Sow several different lettuces, radishes, cabbages and other cool-season crops. Tie the leaves of cauliflower together over the developing heads when they are the size of a silver dollar. Use string or raffia. This produces beautifully blanched, perfectly white heads.

Martin Johnson Heade
(American, 1819-1904)
Passion Flowers and Hummingbirds,
about 1875-1885
Oil on canvas, 15¼ x 21½ inches
Gift of Maxim Karolik for the Karolik
Collection of American Paintings,
1815-1865 47.138

IN BLOOM THIS MONTH
Achimenes, acidanthera, bedding begonia, bignonia, butterfly bush, butterfly weed, campsis, canna, celosia, cleome, cockscomb, cosmos, crape myrtle, dahlia, Gloriosa daisy, daylily (*hemerocallis*), four o'clock (*mirabilis*), gladiolus, goldenrod, morning glory, salvia, silver-lace vine, sunflower, flowering tobacco, trumpet vine, tuberose, water lily and zinnia.

Butterfly bush, *Buddleia* x *davidii* cultivars, produce voluptuous, fragrant flower spikes of red, purple, lavender and white that are almost always hovered over by butterflies. The flowers begin in July, peak in August, and continue into September.

Trumpet creeper, *Campsis radicans*, is a North American native deciduous vine, with orange trumpet flowers produced in abundance midsummer on. There are cultivars having yellow or apricot blossoms, others in bright, clear orange. The species is more saturated red-orange.

Crape myrtle, *Lagerstroemia indica*, shifts into high gear in August, blooming with unbelievable profusion in white, pink, red, purple or violet. There are dwarf forms suited to growing in outdoor planters and hanging baskets.

Henry Roderick Newman (American, 1843-1917)
Wildflowers, 1887
Watercolor on paper, 15 × 10 inches
Gift of Denman W. Ross
17.141

NEW PURCHASES

NEW PLANTINGS

NEW BLOOMINGS

I

HIGH

LOW

PREC.

2

HIGH

LOW

PREC.

3

HIGH

LOW

PREC.

Flower in the crannied wall
I pluck you out of the crannies,
I hold you here, root and all, in my hand,
Little flower—but if I could understand
What you are, root and all, and all in all,
I should know what God and man is.

ALFRED LORD TENNYSON,
"Flower in the Crannied Wall"

4

HIGH

LOW

PREC.

5

HIGH

LOW

PREC.

Pierre Auguste Renoir
(French, 1841-1919)
Girls Picking Flowers in a Meadow
Oil on canvas, 25⅝ × 31⅞ inches
Juliana Cheney Edwards Collection
39.675

6

HIGH

LOW

PREC.

7

HIGH

LOW

PREC.

8

HIGH

LOW

PREC.

9

HIGH

LOW

PREC.

10

HIGH

LOW

PREC.

I was asked, "What is your favourite flower?" The reply seemed almost to suggest itself: "Any flower, turn by turn, which happens to be in season at the moment."

VITA SACKVILLE WEST

11

HIGH

LOW

PREC.

Eleanor Warren Motley
(American, dates unknown)
Purple Petunias
Watercolor, 14¼ × 15¼ inches
Painting Department Special Fund
28.51

12

HIGH

LOW

PREC.

13

HIGH

LOW

PREC.

14

HIGH

LOW

PREC.

15

HIGH

LOW

PREC.

16

HIGH

LOW

PREC.

17

HIGH

LOW

PREC.

18

HIGH

LOW

PREC.

19

HIGH

LOW

PREC.

I should like to enjoy this summer flower by flower, as if it were to be the last one for me.

ANDRE GIDE, *Journals*

20

HIGH

LOW

PREC.

Oscar Claude Monet
(French, 1840-1926)
Waterlilies (I), 1905
Oil on canvas, 35¼ x 39½
Gift of Edward Jackson Holmes.
39.804

21

HIGH

LOW

PREC.

22

HIGH

LOW

PREC.

23

HIGH

LOW

PREC.

24

HIGH

LOW

PREC.

25

HIGH

LOW

PREC.

26

HIGH

LOW

PREC.

Paul Gustave Louis Christophe Doré
(French, 1832-1883)
Summer
Oil on canvas, 104$\frac{7}{8}$ x 78$\frac{3}{4}$ inches
Gift of Richard Baker
73.8

Oscar Claude Monet
(French, 1840-1926)
Flower Beds at Vétheuil, 1881
Oil on canvas, 36¼ x 28⅞ inches
John Pickering Lyman Collection
19.1313

27

HIGH

LOW

PREC.

28

HIGH

LOW

PREC.

29

HIGH

LOW

PREC.

30

HIGH

LOW

PREC.

31

HIGH

LOW

PREC.

SEPTEMBER

GARDEN NOTES

Vines

Cut wisteria back to three to five sets of leaflets, except on the runners needed to extend the coverage of the vine. If you have a tree-form wisteria, cut every vine or branch back to the base set of three to five leaflets. This forces the production of flowering wood. If you have an established wisteria that refuses to flower, take stock of how it is being fertilized. If set in the surround of a lawn that is freely fed high-nitrogen fertilizers, that could explain nonflowering. Applications of low- or no-nitrogen fertlizers such as 1-6-5 or 0-6-5 will encourage wisteria bloom.

> *O Autumn, laden with fruit, and stained*
> *With the blood of the grape, pass not, but sit*
> *Beneath my shady roof; there thou may'st rest*
> *And tune thy jolly voice to my fresh pipe*
> *And all the daughters of the year shall dance!*
> *Sing now the lusty song of fruits and flowers.*
>
> WILLIAM BLAKE, "To Autumn"

Detail of illustration on page 13

Flowers/ground covers

This is the ideal time to make or renovate a bed of lily-of-the-valley, *Convallaria majalis.* Dig clumps with a spading fork. Separate out the best divisions, or "pips." Spade the emptied bed and mix in well-rotted manure or compost. Set the best divisions four to six inches apart. Water well. The bed won't need anything except admiration for the next four to six years. Day lilies (*Hemerocallis*) can also be divided and transplanted now. A bed of them can be renovated in very much the same way as described for lily-of-the-valley.

Shrubs

In the South, the glories of winter-spring such as azalea, camellia and jasmine benefit from deep watering at this season, the time when they are setting buds.

Lawns

No matter where you live or the size lawn you envision, now is one of the most propitious times to start, to patch, to instigate a face-lift. Rye grass may be sown for winter lawns in the deep South. Kentucky bluegrass goes in now for permanent turf in the upper and middle South. Where Japanese beetle grubs are a problem, apply milky spore disease bacteria.

Edibles

Each day leading up to the first frost is another opportunity to harvest fresh sweet basil and to make pesto sauce, surely one of the more delectable and healthful foods that is based on something home-grown. For several hundred years basil has been associated with promoting health and strength in the upper respiratory system. It seems hardly a coincidence that basil's great popularity today has occurred simultaneously with ever-increasing air pollution and lack of quality oxygen.

Fruits

Wait to pick grapes until they are ripe. To protect from birds, tie a small paper bag over each bunch. The original Concord grape is visible from the road in Concord, Massachusetts. It was originated in 1849 by Ephraim Bull.

Evergreens, conifers

This is an ideal time to transplant or set out new specimens, preferably from containers. Prepare just enough soil to accommodate the rootball. Tease some of the endemic soil into what is being added, to help the tree roots become deeply established and self-reliant. Experts say it's not really a good idea to dig the 5 hole for the 50-cent plant, because the effect is to create a container of enriched growing medium, out of which the plant's roots never really establish.

IN BLOOM THIS MONTH

Abelia. Canna. Clematis, sweet autumn and others. Colchicum. Cosmos. Crape myrtle. Crocus, autumn-flowering. Dahlia. Dwarf Japanese knotweed, *Polygonum cuspidatum compactum*. Goldenrod. Leonotis. *Lobelia cardinalis*. Lycoris. Marigold. Mint shrub, *Elsholtzia stauntonii*. Passionflower. Roses. Salvias. Tuberose.

Sweet autumn clematis, *C. maximowicziana* (formerly offered as *C. paniculata*), is a vigorous climber to 30 feet and never lovelier than when it has escaped into the branches of a towering shade tree. The fragrant flowers in late summer-early fall are followed by silvery seed heads.

Japanese knotweed in its dwarf form, *Polygonum cuspidatum compactum*, makes a great show of crimson red flowers, close examination of which reveals their membership in the buckwheat family. This is considered an herbaceous ground cover. The related fleece vine, *P. aubertii*, with white flowers, takes on the shape of whatever it climbs on, ideally a trellis arbor that will help the vine have a classical form in the garden and also show off its leaves and delicate blossoms.

Jean François Millet
(French, 1814-1875)
In the Vineyard
Oil on canvas, 14¾ × 11⅝ inches
Gift of Quincy Adams Shaw through
Quincy A. Shaw, Jr. and Mrs. Marian
Shaw Haughton
17.1487

NEW PURCHASES

NEW PLANTINGS

NEW BLOOMINGS

Paul Gauguin (French, 1848-1903)
Flowers and a Bowl of Fruit on a Table
Oil on canvas mounted on paperboard,
16⅞ × 24¾ inches
Bequest of John T. Spaulding
48.546

Doesn't it seem as if autumn were the real creator, more creative than the spring, which all at once is, more creative when it comes with its will to change, and destroys the much-too-finished, the much-too-satisfied, indeed almost bourgeouis-comfortable picture of summer?

RAINER MARIE RILKE, "Letters"

I

HIGH

LOW

PREC.

2

HIGH

LOW

PREC.

3

HIGH

LOW

PREC.

4

HIGH

LOW

PREC.

5

HIGH

LOW

PREC.

6

HIGH

LOW

PREC.

Charles Emile Heil
(American, 1870-1950)
Lotus
Watercolor, 16 × 22 inches
Museum Purchase
43.1310

7

HIGH

LOW

PREC.

8

HIGH

LOW

PREC.

9

HIGH

LOW

PREC.

10

HIGH

LOW

PREC.

11

HIGH

LOW

PREC.

12

HIGH

LOW

PREC.

Anonymous (German 17th century)
after Basilius Besler
(German, 1561-1629)
Sunflower from *Hortus Eystettensis,*
Nuremberg, 1713
Hand colored engraving,
20½ × 16¾ inches
Bequest of the Estate of George P. Dike,
Elita R. Dike Collection
69.97

13

HIGH

LOW

PREC.

14

HIGH

LOW

PREC.

15

HIGH

LOW

PREC.

16

HIGH

LOW

PREC.

To me the meanest flower that blows can give
Thoughts that do often lie too deep for tears.

WILLIAM WORDSWORTH,
"Intimations of Immortality"

Jacob Abraham Camille Pissarro
(Danish [worked in France], 1830-1903)
Woman Emptying a Wheelbarrow
Drypoint and aquatint,
17⅛ × 12 inches (sheet)
Lee M. Friedman Fund
1975.360

17

HIGH

LOW

PREC.

Everything grows for everybody. Everything dies for everybody too . . . There are no green thumbs or black thumbs. There are only gardeners and non-gardeners.

HENRY MITCHELL, *The Essential Earthman*

18

HIGH

LOW

PREC.

19

HIGH

LOW

PREC.

20

HIGH

LOW

PREC.

21

HIGH

LOW

PREC.

22

HIGH

LOW

PREC.

23

HIGH

LOW

PREC.

24

HIGH

LOW

PREC.

25

HIGH

LOW

PREC.

26

HIGH

LOW

PREC.

27

HIGH

LOW

PREC.

28

HIGH

LOW

PREC.

29

HIGH

LOW

PREC.

30

HIGH

LOW

PREC.

John La Farge
(American, 1835-1910)
Hollyhocks and Corn, 1865
Oil on panel, 23½ × 16½ in.
Gift of Dr. William Sturgis Bigelow
21.1442

OCTOBER

GARDEN NOTES

Composting

If you do not yet have a compost pile, there is no moment better to start than right now. Every garden produces a tremendous amount of organic waste at the end of the active growing season. Prepare to recycle all of it so that future gardening projects can be more successful and you won't have to spend money for soil amendments. The pile can be contained with wire hardware cloth and stakes, with boards, bricks or concrete blocks, or by a ready-made, self-contained composting unit that makes it all clean and attractive in even the smallest of back yards and outdoor living areas.

Fertilize spring-blooming shrubs lightly with four parts superphosphate mixed with one part sulfur of potash. Do not use a fertilizer with nitrogen on this type of plant in the fall, as it would cause rapid new growth soon to be killed by winter cold.

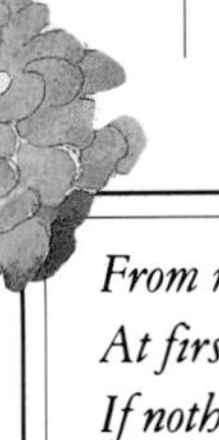

From morning suns and evening dews
At first thy little being came:
If nothing once, you nothing lose,
For when you die, you are the same;
The space between is but an hour
The frail duration of a flower.

PHILIP FRENEAU, "The Wild Honeysuckle"

Flowers

Forget-me-nots, violas, pansies, wallflowers — now is the time to set them over beds of spring-flowering bulbs, especially tulips. Any of these carpeters also looks lovely on its own, in a bed or a container.

Trees, shrubs

Fall is one of the year's best seasons for planting and transplanting most but not all woodies. If in doubt, ask a local nursery or botanical garden expert. The soil is more likely to be warm, moist and friable — "workable" — in the fall than it is in the spring. The air may be nippy, but that means the plant's top parts won't have to work so hard. Meanwhile, the warm, moist earth encourages rapid expansion of the feeder roots that will sustain the plant through winter and place it at an advantage over the same plant in the same situation planted in the spring.

Bulbs

Set out spring-flowering bulbs beginning as soon as they are available. The small bulbs such as crocus and snowdrops go in first, followed by narcissus and daffodils, then hyacinths; tulips can go in last, just before the last call represented by killing frost and crusting of the surface soil. Bulb fertilizer is now considered better to use than bone meal. True steamed bone meal has become prohibitively expensive. Also, mixing it into newly cultivated soil invites various digging creatures such as squirrels and raccoons that will in the process decimate your bulb plantings and eat everything except the narcissus and daffodil bulbs, these being poisonous.

Roses

Some of the season's loveliest blooms appear at the last gasp of growth. Never mind that the bushes have lost most of their leaves to mildew and black spot, just enjoy the blossoms and take time to appreciate their unique and individual scents. It is a good time for sanitation, however, so keep the discolored or diseased leaves promptly picked or raked up. Don't add these to your regular compost pile. Quietly bury them in some out-of-the-way spot. In the deep South, give roses a shot of 0-10-10 to harden off the wood and prepare them for a little winter rest.

Shrubs

Lilacs and crape myrtles often become quite silvered with powdery mildew by this time. Don't bother to spray. Frost will soon end their season, and the leaves have already done their work this time around.

Charles Demuth
(American, 1883-1935)
***Zinnias and Daisies*, 1925**
Watercolor, 17½ x 11⅝ inches
Frederick Brown Fund
40.231

IN BLOOM THIS MONTH

Amaranthus, or Joseph's coat. Hardy aster. Bedding begonia. Chrysanthemum. Dahlia. Elaeagnus. Gardenia. Jasmine such as *Jasminum tortuosum* and *J. nitidum*, and jessamine such as *Cestrum nocturnum*. Marigold. Monkshood *Aconitum napellus*. Ornamental grasses such as *Miscanthus*, *Erianthus ravennae* and *Cortaderia selloana*. Narcissus, fall-blooming types such as early paper-whites. Roses. Salvia. Tea-olive, *Osmanthus fragrans*. *Tibouchina* or glory-bush. Tuberose. It is also the time of most glorious fall foliage color. If you want a particular hue of a special kind of plant, best purchase it in fall leaf color as a container specimen.

Tea-olive, *Osmanthus fragrans*, is one of the most powerfully and pleasantly scented of all fragrant flowers. The individual blossoms, pale creamy white, are hardly as big as the end of your little finger, yet one is sufficient to lightly scent an entire room. The plant tolerates cold to around 25° F.

Bedding begonias are never lovelier than at the end of the season outdoors. They pot up readily. Use a trowel or gardener's shovel. Take a soil ball about the same diameter as the plant and a couple of inches deep. Set in prepared bulb pans or azalea pots. Moisten well. Keep in a sunny, airy place, and the plants will hardly appear to have been transplanted.

NEW PURCHASES

NEW PLANTINGS

NEW BLOOMINGS

Jean Françcois Millet
(French, 1814-1875)
Man Turning over the Soil
Oil on canvas, 9⅞ x 12¾ inches
Gift of Quincy Adams Shaw through
Quincy A. Shaw, Jr. and Mrs. Marian
Shaw Haughton
17.1488

There is life in the ground; it goes into the seeds and it also, when it is stirred up, goes into the man who stirs it.

CHARLES DUDLEY WARNER

1

HIGH

LOW

PREC.

2

HIGH

LOW

PREC.

3

HIGH

LOW

PREC.

4

HIGH

LOW

PREC.

5

HIGH

LOW

PREC.

Henry G. Keller
(American, 1870-1949)
Still Life with Fruit and Flowers
Watercolor, 15¼ × 22 inches
Gift of the Ace of Clubs through
Mrs. Bernard R. Baldwin
42.420

6

HIGH

LOW

PREC.

7

HIGH

LOW

PREC.

8

HIGH

LOW

PREC.

9

HIGH

LOW

PREC.

10

HIGH

LOW

PREC.

11

HIGH

LOW

PREC.

12

HIGH

LOW

PREC.

13

HIGH

LOW

PREC.

A flowerless room is a soul-less room, to my thinking; but even one solitary little vase of a living flower may redeem it.

VITA SACKVILLE-WEST, *Garden Book*

14

HIGH

LOW

PREC.

Hermann Dudley Murphy
(American, 1867-1945)
Zinnias and Marigolds, 1933
Oil on canvas, 30 x 25 inches
The Hayden Collection
43.30

15

HIGH

LOW

PREC.

16

HIGH

LOW

PREC.

17

HIGH

LOW

PREC.

18

HIGH

LOW

PREC.

19

HIGH

LOW

PREC.

Stanton Macdonald-Wright
(American, 1890-1973)
Still Life with Arum Lilies and Fruit, 1923
Oil on canvas, 22 x 18 inches
Bequest of John T. Spaulding
48.575

S.Macdonald-Wright

20

HIGH

LOW

PREC.

21

HIGH

LOW

PREC.

22

HIGH

LOW

PREC.

23

HIGH

LOW

PREC.

24

HIGH

LOW

PREC.

25

HIGH

LOW

PREC.

26

HIGH

LOW

PREC.

Edouard Vuillard
(French, 1868-1940)
Woman Sewing before a Garden Window, 1895
Oil on paper mounted on canvas, mounted on panel
12½ x 14⅜
Bequest of John T. Spaulding
48.612

27

HIGH

LOW

PREC.

28

HIGH

LOW

PREC.

29

HIGH

LOW

PREC.

30

HIGH

LOW

PREC.

31

HIGH

LOW

PREC.

Frederick Childe Hassam
(American, 1859-1935)
Woods in the Fall
Watercolor, 14 x 10 inches
Bequest of Kathleen Rothe
65.1300

NOVEMBER

GARDEN NOTES

Houseplants

As the heating system has to be activated, some indoor plants will require more water. It will also help to use pebble humidity trays, and in any room where many plants are concentrated, it may be a good idea to operate a cool-vapor humidifier. Air containing 30 to 50 percent relative humidity feels comfortable at around 70° F. whereas very dry air, with perhaps less than 10 percent humidity, feels cold at 75° F. Misting the leaves with tepid water helps remove dust and constitutes beneficial therapy for the gardener, but does not appreciably increase relative humidity.

> *No warmth, no cheerfulness, no healthful ease,*
> *No comfortable feel in any member—*
> *No shade, no shine, no butterflies, no bees,*
> *No fruits, no flowers, no leaves, no birds,*
> *November!*
>
> THOMAS HOOD

Orchids, bromeliads, aroids, generiads

The more epiphytic sorts need special attention when they are housebound. Dunk those that are bark-mounted almost daily in lukewarm water, at least when the weather is warm and sunny. On cool, cloudy days, at least give each a good misting. In a greenhouse or plant room where humidity can be maintained at 50 percent or more, less dunking and misting will be needed. *Dendrobium nobile* orchids need to be cool (50-60° F.), sunny and quite dry at this time, dry enough to cause many of the leaves to yellow, shrivel and fall off. This hardening process stirs the flower buds into action and needs to be continued until about midwinter. Then an increase in watering, temperature and humidity will bring on the flower show in a matter of weeks.

Holiday Plants

If you have a poinsettia you want to bloom for next month's holidays, be sure that the plant receives no light except from the sun. This means it cannot stand in a room where electric lights are burned or the television is operated, either before sunrise or after sunset. Poinsettia does need moderate to warm temperatures and lots of bright sunlight at this time, also ample water so that the leaves do not wilt.

Paper-whites for Christmas: Set the bulbs to root around November 10–20, in order to have lots of flowers by the third or fourth week of December. Allow about two-three weeks in a cool, dark place for lots of roots to form, then bring to a cool, sunny, airy place.

Flowers

Don't apply winter mulches or side-dressings of half-rotted compost or manure until after killing frost and the ground has frozen. If mulches are applied too early they may keep the soil from freezing at the proper time and thus render roots ill prepared for the extreme cold that comes later on. When you are applying side-dressings through a bed of perennial flowers, take care that most of it is around them, not directly on top of the crowns.

Trees, shrubs, evergreens

Newly planted specimens as well as older ones in exposed situations will benefit from a coating of anti-desiccant spray. This keeps moisture inside during the trying, drying winds that sweep over most gardens in winter.

A rainy, cold day this month often turns out to be the ideal time to straighten the garden-tool storage shed. Winterize power tools. Make notes in your garden datebook, reminders you'll need next spring about things to do or tools, supplies and miscellaneous garden gear that will need restocking before another season.

Severin Roesen
(American, born Germany, ?-1871)
Still Life — Flowers in a Basket
Oil on canvas, 30 x 40¼ inches
Purchased M. and M. Karolik Fund
69.1228

IN BLOOM THIS MONTH

Camellia japonica. C. sasanqua. Chrysanthemum. Dahlia. Pansy. Roses. Sweet olive *(Osmanthus fragrans).* Highbush blueberry, *Vaccinium corymbosum,* has edible blueberries in summer and at this time the fall foliage is brilliant red; excellent in the garden or as a containerized shrub. Japanese maples, *Acer palmatum* varieties, are at their most glorious in the last sunny moments before winter sets in with a killing frost. Bald cypress, *Taxodium distichum,* turns pinkish beige with the arrival of autumn. The fruit of Japanese beauty berry, *Callicarpa japonica,* is its most shiny, waxy red-violet-purple at this time. There are also the blue fruits of porcelain vine, *Ampelopsis brevipedunculata,* and the glowing orange-red of Oriental bittersweet, *Celastrus orbiculatus.* Native witch-hazel, *Hamamelis virginiana,* is one of the latest shrubs to bloom, small, spidery yellow blossoms that can be readily overlooked amongst the brilliant . yellow-gold of the leaves. The flowering branches are lovely cut and brought inside, especially if all the leaves are first removed, so as to emphasize the unusual, scented blossoms.

Some of the year's loveliest dahlia blossoms are produced in the very last days of the season. Sometimes they can be saved from premature frost by covering on cold nights with plastic or cloth, so that an extended season of flowering can occur during Indian summer. This is also true of many chrysanthemums, especially those that bloom naturally quite late in the season.

NEW PURCHASES

NEW PLANTINGS

NEW BLOOMINGS

There was a child went forth every day, And the first object he look'd upon, that object he became
The early lilacs became a part of this child,
And grass and white and red morning-glories, and white and red clover, and the song of the phoebe-bird

WALT WHITMAN, "There Was a Child Went Forth"

John Singer Sargent
(American, 1856-1925)
Miss Helen Sears, 1895
Oil on canvas, 65¾ x 35¾ inches
Gift of Mrs. J. D. Cameron Bradley
55.1116

1

HIGH

LOW

PREC.

2

HIGH

LOW

PREC.

3

HIGH

LOW

PREC.

4

HIGH

LOW

PREC.

5

HIGH

LOW

PREC.

6

HIGH

LOW

PREC.

How sad would be November
If we had no knowledge
of the Spring.

EDWIN WAY TEALE

George C. Lambdin
(American, 1830-1896)
Vase of Flowers, 1875
Oil on canvas, 16 x 12 inches
Bequest of Maxim Karolik
64.458

7

HIGH

LOW

PREC.

8

HIGH

LOW

PREC.

9

HIGH

LOW

PREC.

10

HIGH

LOW

PREC.

11

HIGH

LOW

PREC.

12

HIGH

LOW

PREC.

13

HIGH

LOW

PREC.

Jean François Millet
(French, 1814-1875)
Farmyard by Moonlight
Pastel and black conté crayon on paper, 27⅞ × 34⅛ inches
Gift of Quincy Adams Shaw through Quincy A. Shaw, Jr. and Mrs. Marian Shaw Haughton
17.1525

14

HIGH

LOW

PREC.

15

HIGH

LOW

PREC.

16

HIGH

LOW

PREC.

17

HIGH

LOW

PREC.

The fairest thing in nature, a flower,
still has its roots in earth and manure.

D.H. LAWRENCE, *Letters*

18

HIGH

LOW

PREC.

Jean François Millet
(French, 1814-1875)
Primroses
Pastel on paper, 15⅞ × 18⅞ inches
Gift of Quincy Adams Shaw through
Quincy A. Shaw, Jr. and Mrs. Marian
Shaw Haughton
17.1523

19

HIGH

LOW

PREC.

20

HIGH

LOW

PREC.

And God said, "Let the earth bring forth grass, the herb yielding seed, and the fruit tree yielding fruit after his kind, whose seed is in itself upon the earth: and it was so.

GENESIS. 1:11

21

HIGH

LOW

PREC.

22

HIGH

LOW

PREC.

23

HIGH

LOW

PREC.

24

HIGH

LOW

PREC.

25

HIGH

LOW

PREC.

Ignace Henri Jean Théodore
Fantin-Latour (French, 1836-1904)
Flowers and Fruit on a Table, 1865
Oil on canvas, 23⅝ x 28⅞ inches
Bequest of John T. Spaulding
48.540

26

HIGH

LOW

PREC.

27

HIGH

LOW

PREC.

28

HIGH

LOW

PREC.

29

HIGH

LOW

PREC.

How precious are the flowers of mid-winter.... the genuine toughs that for some strange reason elect to display themselves out-of-doors at this time of year.

VITA SACKVILLE-WEST

30

HIGH

LOW

PREC.

Victor (French, 1759–1840),
after P.J. Redouté (French, 1759–1840)
Oreilles d'Ours: Primula auricula
Stipple engraving, printed in color and handcolored, 1st state from Redouté, *Choix des Plus Belles Fleurs* (Paris, 1827)
8¼ x 10¾ inches
Bequest of Estate of George P. Dike, and Elita R. Dike Collection
69.291

Oreilles d'Ours.
Primula Auricula Var.
P. J. Redouté.
Victor

DECEMBER

GARDEN NOTES

All Christmas trees, whether living or cut, last better in a room where temperatures are mostly on the cool side, certainly below 70° F., and shielded from direct drafts of forced air from the heating system. If you select a living tree, coat the needled branches with an antidesiccant so they will be able to retain enough moisture to survive the Christmas season indoors.

Set up bird feeding and watering stations, but only if you are prepared to refill and follow up almost daily.

In the deep South, now's the time to plant amaryllis *(Hippeastrum)*. alpinia or shell ginger, crinum or milk-and-white lily, eucharis and xanthosoma. In the Southwest, bulbs such as these can be planted now: anemone, ranunculus, zephyranthes, ismene, yellow calla-lily, lachenalia. In any mild but cool climate, indoors or out, freesia corms planted now will give spring bloom.

Did you ever meet a gardener who, however fair his ground, was absolutely content and pleased... Is there not always a tree to be felled, a bed to be turfed?... Is there not ever some grand mistake to be remedied next summer?

DEAN HOLE, *A Book About Roses*

Seed and nursery catalogs were once mailed to arrive immediately after the beginning of the New Year. Now the marketers are mailing earlier and earlier, hoping to catch our attention before holiday madness, or maybe offering the hopeful catalogs as a sort of antidote to end-of-the-year blues. At any rate, catalogs are more enjoyable if filed in alphabetical sequence, the old ones discarded to make way for the new editions — unless you have made notes in an old one and need to keep it for reference.

Save wood ashes from the fireplace, as they are a potent source of potash, an essential plant food, and especially appropriate for side dressing in the spring around herbaceous peonies and lilac bushes.

Vines

Tie in place any long, whipping or loose canes on climbing and rambler roses.

Trees

Install wire hardware cloth around the trunks of any trees that are vulnerable to winter attack by beavers, rabbits or other gnawing creatures.

Edibles

Top-dress the kitchen garden with compost or half-rotted manure. It can be spread on generously after the ground freezes, to six inches deep and more. Amazing beneficial action takes place during the alternate freezing and thawing actions of winter.

Start sprouts indoors — alfalfa, radish, mustard, mung bean. They are so quick and easy, so nutritious, so satisfying to the gardener, who gets an emotional charge from helping grow the sprouts, then benefits from eating them.

Flowers

In warmer regions a fertilizer such as 13-13-13 can be applied now to established trees, spring-blooming shrubs, spuria irises and sweet peas (but not until they are a foot tall). Louisiana iris will benefit from a side-dressing ofcottonseed meal and well-rotted manure. Pansies will bloom longer with larger flowers if they are regularly fertilized and if spent blossoms are promptly picked off. This gives the beds a shipshape appearance and means there will be much more color over an extended season.

Bulbs

In the deep South, tulip bulbs are taken out of cold storage and planted in the ground this month. Elsewhere, if you had tulips or other hardy spring-flowering bulbs that for one reason or another didn't get into the earth before winter freeze-up, they can be potted now in bulb pans or azalea pots, using any all-purpose potting soil. Keep them evenly moist and cool, around 40° F. in a dark place, for a rooting period of eight to twelve weeks. Next, after roots are filling the pots, bring the bulbs to a sunny, airy, cool window or light garden. They will come into bloom in a few weeks but must never lack plenty of water.

IN BLOOM THIS MONTH

Japanese winterberry, *Ilex serrata*, is a multibranched shrub with tiny red fruit, especially showy at this time and when there is newly fallen snow. Winterberry, *Ilex verticillata*, is a deciduous species with bare branches covered with red berries at this time of year, orange or yellow in other varieties at this time of year. The scarlet pea-sized fruit of Chinese stranvaesia, *Stranvaesia davidiana*, is especially showy against the bronzy foliage. Autumn flowering cherry, *Prunus subhirtella* 'Autumnalis' is a small- to medium-sized deciduous tree that produces an abundance of semidouble, pale pink flowers that bloom during warm periods, first in late fall or earliest winter, again in the spring (early April). In warmer regions, plants for show at this time include sweet alyssum, bougainvillea, calendula or pot-marigold, early cultivars of *Camellia japonica* and *C. sasanqua*, bedding geranium, Chinese hibiscus, *Jasminum nitidum*, pansy, petunia, pinks, poinsettia, roses, sweet olive and violet.

Jan van Huysum
(Dutch, 1682-1749)
Vase of Flowers in a Niche
Oil on panel, 35 × 27½ inches
Bequest of Stanton Blake
89.503

NEW PURCHASES

NEW PLANTINGS

NEW BLOOMINGS

John Singer Sargent
(American, 1856-1925)
The Garden Wall, 1910
Watercolor on paper,
15¾ × 20½ inches
Hayden Collection. Charles Henry
Hayden Fund 12.222

No occupation is so delightful to me as the culture of the earth, and no culture comparable to that of the garden. I am still devoted to the garden. But though an old man, I am but a young gardener.

THOMAS JEFFERSON

1

HIGH

LOW

PREC.

2

HIGH

LOW

PREC.

3

HIGH

LOW

PREC.

4

HIGH

LOW

PREC.

5

HIGH

LOW

PREC.

6

HIGH

LOW

PREC.

Full many a flower is born to blush unseen, And waste its sweetness on the desert air.

THOMAS GRAY,
"Elegy Written in a Country Churchyard"

7

HIGH

LOW

PREC.

Joseph Stella
(American, 1877-1946)
Cactus and Tropical Foliage,
about 1922
Watercolor over graphite,
18⅛ x 24⅛ inches
Sophie M. Friedman Fund
1984.412

8

HIGH

LOW

PREC.

9

HIGH

LOW

PREC.

10

HIGH

LOW

PREC.

11

HIGH

LOW

PREC.

12

HIGH

LOW

PREC.

Jean Désiré Gustave Courbet
(French, 1819-1877)
Hollyhocks in a Copper Bowl, 1872
Oil on canvas, 23⅝ × 19¼ inches
Bequest of John T. Spaulding
48.530

The more one gardens, the more one learns; and the more one learns, the more one realizes how little one knows. I suppose the whole of life is like that: the endless complications, the endless difficulties, the endless fight against one thing or another, whether it be green-fly on the roses or the complexity of personal relationships.

VITA SACKVILLE-WEST, *A Joy of Gardening*

13

HIGH

LOW

PREC.

14

HIGH

LOW

PREC.

15

HIGH

LOW

PREC.

16

HIGH

LOW

PREC.

French, Anonymous (17th century)
Flowers, Butterfly and Book
Oil on panel, 10½ × 14¼ inches
Gift of Mrs. Maxim Karolik for the Karolik Collection of American Paintings 1815-1865
47.1252

17

HIGH

LOW

PREC.

18

HIGH

LOW

PREC.

At Christmas I no more desire a rose
Than wish a snow in May's newfangled mirth;
But like of each thing that in season grows.

WILLIAM SHAKESPEARE, *Love's Labour's Lost*

19

HIGH
LOW
PREC.

20

HIGH
LOW
PREC.

21

HIGH
LOW
PREC.

22

HIGH
LOW
PREC.

23

HIGH
LOW
PREC.

24

HIGH

LOW

PREC.

25

HIGH

LOW

PREC.

Cedar Bird (Plate XLIII)
Etching and aquatint
with hand-coloring
in watercolor
by Robert Havell, Jr.
(English, 1793-1878) after
John James Audubon
(American, 1785-1851)
From *Birds of America*,
1827-1838
19⅝ x 12¼ inches
Gift of William Hooper, 1921
21.11772.43

26

HIGH

LOW

PREC.

27

HIGH

LOW

PREC.

28

HIGH

LOW

PREC.

29

HIGH

LOW

PREC.

30

HIGH

LOW

PREC.

Erastus Salisbury Field
(American, 1805-1900)
The Garden of Eden
Oil on canvas
34¾ x 46 inches
Gift of Maxim Karolik for the
Karolik Collection of
American Paintings, 1815-1865
48.1027

31

HIGH

LOW

PREC.

It is not graceful and it makes one hot, but it is a blessed sort of work, and if Eve had had a spade in Paradise and known what to do with it, we should not have had all that sad business of the apple.

COUNTESS VON ARNIM,
"Elizabeth and her German Garden"

Name	Phone	Address	Service or Product

Name	Phone	Address	Service or Product

Sketch your garden on these pages, Draw permanent boundaries and structures (house, walls, pipes) first, then pencil in plants.

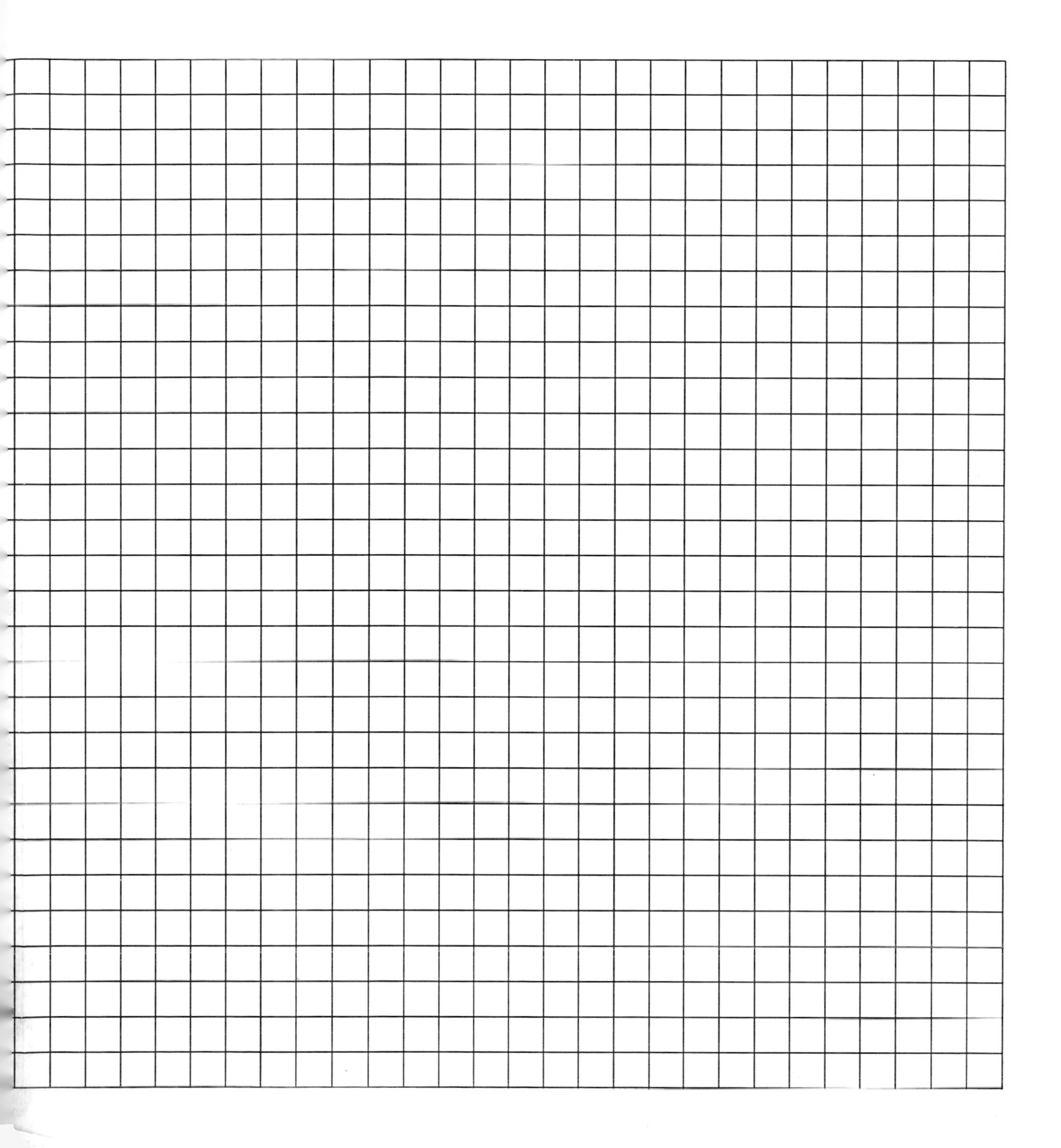